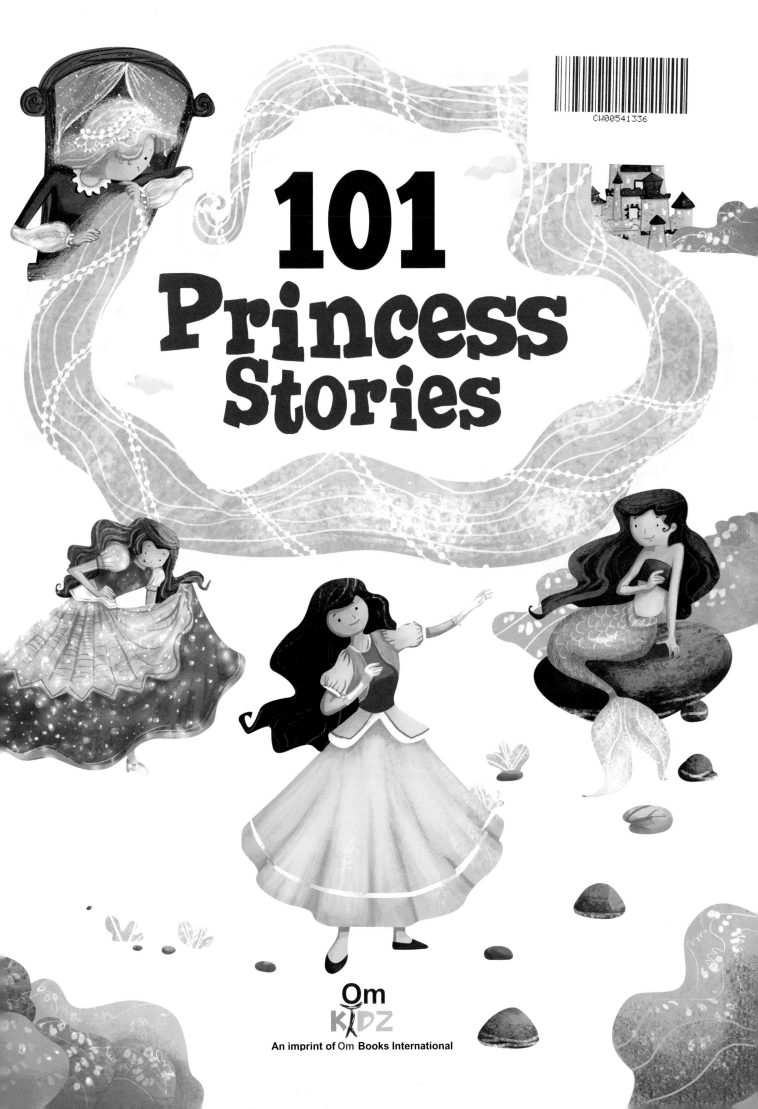

101
Princess Stories

Om
KIDZ
An imprint of Om Books International

Contents

1. The Lark's Feather

Once, a man had three daughters. One day, he set out on a long journey. He promised to bring pearls and diamonds for the two elder girls. The youngest daughter asked for a singing lark. When it was time for him to return home, the man could not find a lark. Then, he spotted one in a forest. As the man tried to catch it, a lion guarding the lark, sprang towards him. The lion allowed the man to take the lark on one condition. The man would have to send him its feathers with his daughter.

Unhappy, the man went home to his youngest daughter. He told her of the lion's condition. The girl smiled, fearlessly. The next morning, she went into the forest. She kept the lark's feathers before the lion. Magically, he turned into a prince. He had been under a spell. The grateful prince married the youngest daughter.

2. The Kind-hearted Girl

Once there lived a little girl who lost her parents and she had no home. She only had some clothes on and some bread. One day while walking on the road, a poor man begged the girl for food. She gave him her bread and went ahead. As she moved a little ahead, she found a boy whose head was cold, so she gave him her hat. Then, she saw a girl shivering with cold. She pitied the poor girl and covered her with her jacket. Soon, she entered a forest and met another girl. As she had no clothes on, the kind girl gave her frock to that girl.

Suddenly, lots of money started pouring down from Heaven on her. Magically, there were new clothes on her body. God had been watching the kind-hearted little girl and this was her reward. She became rich and lived happily ever after.

3. The Girl and the Witch

Once, a little girl and a little boy were playing together in a rose garden. Sadly, the boy went missing.

The girl wondered if he had drowned in the river. Thus, she went to the river and climbed into a boat. Soon, it started drifting down the river. The little girl was scared and started crying. Then she saw a small, colourful house with a beautiful garden. Just then a witch who lived there, came to the riverside. She was a good witch and so helped the girl out of the boat. The witch comforted the girl and let her stay with her for as long as she wanted. The girl soon forgot all about her friend and her home, too. However, after a few days, the girl saw the rose bushes in the witch's garden, and they reminded her of home.

The girl at once ran towards the river. She found a boat there which was being rowed by her friend. The children rowed back home to reunite with their happy parents.

4. Rumpelstiltskin

Once, a king asked a miller's daughter to spin straw into gold. An elf offered to help her, but he said, "Promise me that you will give me your first-born."

The girl agreed and the elf spun the gold. The girl took it to the king. He was very pleased and married her. A year went by and a baby was born to the girl, now the queen. Soon after, the elf appeared and asked for the baby. The queen pleaded with the elf.

However, if she could guess his name in the next three days, he would leave the baby. Two days went by and the queen was sad. She still didn't know the elf's name. Just then, her maid came and said, "I saw a small man sing that his name was 'Rumpelstiltskin' and that he would soon get the queen's baby!"

The queen went to meet the elf. She told him that his name was Rumpelstiltskin. This enraged the elf so much that he went away stomping, never to come back again!

5. Thrushbeard

A proud princess rejected all her suitors. She especially made fun of a prince by calling him "Thrushbeard." Her father was very angry and married her to a beggar. The beggar took the princess across many places that belonged to Prince Thrushbeard. The beggar asked the princess to work for a living, but she failed at everything! One day, while the princess was selling pots, a horseman destroyed them. So, her husband got her a job as a maid in the king's palace.

Now, a feast was being arranged at the palace to celebrate the marriage of the king's son. The princess secretly peeped through the curtains to look at the preparations. Suddenly, Thrushbeard pulled her into the party. Then he told her that he had disguised as a beggar for her love, and wanted her to lose her pride. The princess was very happy and they lived happily thereafter.

6. The Princess and the Frog

Long ago, there lived a king who had a beautiful daughter. One day, the princess was playing in the forest when her ball fell in a fountain. Suddenly, a frog came out and said, "I will get your ball. But you will have to love me in return." The princess agreed. But just as the frog got her ball out, the princess ran away. The next day, the frog reached the king's palace. He told the king about the princess's promise. The king said, "My dear, the frog helped you, now you should fulfill your promise." Thus, the frog started living with the princess. With time, she started liking him a lot.

Then, one day, the frog changed into a handsome prince. He said, "A curse had changed me into a frog. Your true love has broken that curse." The princess was very happy. Soon, they both were married and lived happily ever after.

7. Betty's Laziness

Betty lived with her parents. She had one bad habit. She always made some excuse to sleep till late. Every day, her mother shouted, "Get up Betty, otherwise you will miss your school bus." But Betty would not listen. Betty often missed her school bus and her father had to drop her to school. But she did not seem to bother.

One day, Betty's father was not at home. As usual, she got late and missed her bus. Her mother hired a taxi and dropped her to the school, but by then the gates of the school had closed.

Betty had a painting competition that day. She requested the guards to let her in, but they refused. So, she had to go back home with her mother.

Betty loved painting and missed the competition due to her bad habit. She realised her mistake and from that day she woke up on time.

8. The Wish-granting Fish

A fisherman lived with his wife in a pigsty. One day, while fishing, he caught a big fish. It said, "I am not a fish, but an enchanted prince. Please let me go."
The fisherman felt sorry and let it go.

However, his wife wanted him to ask the fish to give them a hut. The fisherman did so, and the fish granted the wish. Thereafter, the wife wanted a big castle. The fish granted that wish, too.

The wife, next, wanted to be the queen. So, the fish made her the queen. The wife then said, "I want to be the empress of this kingdom." The fish fulfilled her wish. Then the wife said, "I wish to be God."

When the fisherman went to the fish with this request, it said, "That is impossible! She is only fit to live in a pigsty!" Thus, the fisherman and his wife had to live in a pigsty all their life for being greedy.

9. Jorinda and Joringel

Once, an old witch lived in a castle in a forest. Now, if a pretty maiden wandered close to her castle, the witch turned her into a bird. She kept all the birds in a cage. The witch turned young boys into statues and left them outside her castle. When their spell broke, they went back. Jorinda and Joringel were a couple who had just been engaged.

One day, they wandered too close to the castle. Jorinda became a nightingale and Joringel a statue! The witch appeared, put Jorinda in a cage and took her away. When Joringel came alive, he looked for ways to free Jorinda.

He found a blood red flower with a pearl in its centre. He took this flower to the castle. Joringel touched the witch with the flower, which took away all her magical powers. He also used the flower to turn Jorinda back to a human being along with all the other captured maidens. Jorinda and Joringel lived happily ever after.

10. Anna's Lesson

Anna was a little girl, who loved to dance. Her Mother noticed her interest and decided to make her join the Ballet School.

Anna was very excited about learning ballet. She put together her ballet dress and shoes and went to the Ballet School with her Mother.

However, when the class began, Anna saw that the teacher, Mr. Harrison, was very strict. He would scold the students if they did not dance properly. Anna felt so scared that she could not dance correctly at all. Mr. Harrison scolded her, too.

Anna ran home in tears and told her Mother about Mr. Harrison. Mother hugged her and said, "Anna, the teacher scolds you because he wants you to become a perfect dancer. Listen carefully to what he says and concentrate on the lesson. Remember that you love to dance!"

Anna understood her Mother's words. She wiped her tears and said, "You are right, Mother. I will do my best to learn ballet."

11. Garden Fairies

Jenny lived in a cottage. She had a lovely garden outside the cottage. A few fairies lived in Jenny's garden. The Flower Fairy coloured all the flowers and gave them their fragrance. One day, she fell ill and was advised to take rest. The Queen Fairy said, "I will assign your work to Flounder and Mischief, two other fairies."

Now, Flounder and Mischief were very naughty. They coloured the bluebells yellow and the sunflowers blue. Also, they made the roses smell like jasmine!

Next morning, Jenny went to the garden and was shocked. She immediately called the Flower Fairy. When the Flower Fairy saw her garden in such a mess, she went and complained to the Queen Fairy.

The Queen ordered to make everything in the garden normal like before. So, the bluebells were blue and sunflowers were yellow, again. Also, the roses and jasmine got their own fragrances back.

Jenny was happy now.

12. The Golden Egg

One day, a farmer found a golden egg in his hen house. He happily showed it to his wife.

The next day, the farmer's wife caught the hen that laid the golden egg. She rushed to the farmer with the hen and said, "We'll never have to work again!"

The farmer built a special coop for the hen and kept her separate from the others. Every morning, the hen laid a golden egg and the farmer grew rich.

However, as their riches increased, they also grew greedier. They were not satisfied with one golden egg a day. "If we could get all the golden eggs together from the hen, we could get richer faster," the farmer's wife said. "The gold must be hidden inside the hen."

The farmer and his wife cut open the hen's stomach to take out the gold. However, they found no gold inside and they never got any more gold.

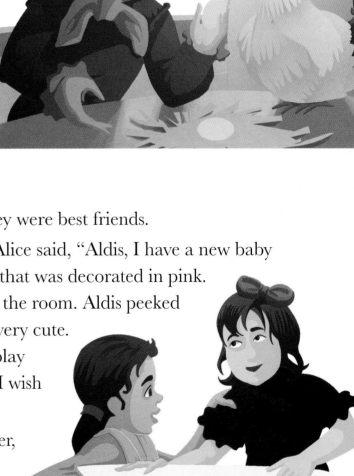

13. Baby Sister

There were two girls, named Alice and Aldis. They were best friends.

One day, Aldis went to Alice's house to play. Alice said, "Aldis, I have a new baby sister. Come and see." Alice took Aldis to a room that was decorated in pink. There was a beautiful white crib in the middle of the room. Aldis peeked into the crib and saw a little baby. The baby was very cute. Alice said, "Isn't my sister pretty? I can't wait to play with her." Aldis said, "Yes Alice, she is very sweet. I wish I had a sister like that."

Aldis ran home to her Mother and said, "Mother, I want a baby sister just like Alice's. She looks so sweet, just like a doll!" Mom smiled, "Sure, Aldis! We will also have a baby in our house, after we celebrate your next birthday." Aldis was very happy. She said, "Thank you very much, Mother."

14. Sharing and Caring

Nellie and Adele were decorating the Christmas tree in their living room. Nellie said, "Have you made your Christmas wish?"

"I have written to Santa, but I won't tell you!" Adele said. The girls were very excited that Christmas was almost there. When they hung up all the decorations on the tree, Nellie said, "Let's make cards for our friends!"

So, the girls started making cards for each of their friends, wishing them a happy Christmas and New Year. They used bright paints and craft paper. Then, Adele said, "Nellie, now I am making one for you. But you have to wait until Christmas to open it."

"I'll make one for you, too. You will be surprised when you see it!" said Nellie.

Laughing, the two girls finished their cards and went to bed. Both were very happy and understood that the true spirit of Christmas was in sharing and caring.

15. Suzanne's Friends

Once, there lived a little girl named Suzanne. She had many friends. One day, Suzanne fell terribly sick. She could not go out to play with her friends now. She did not have the energy to even get up and walk.

Her friends came to know about her illness. They visited her house every day. They brought beautiful flowers and books for her. Some of them even sat at her bedside and read out stories to her.

When Suzanne started feeling better, she could get up and sit on her bed. Her friends took her out for walks in the meadows. It was spring and Suzanne felt happy to see the butterflies and colourful flowers. They also brought tasty pudding and pies for her to eat.

Soon, Suzanne's health improved. She thanked all her friends, for it was because of their help that she got better. It is good to have friends!

16. Lonely Jenny

Jenny's parents worked in the bakery. So, Jenny was left alone at home. She took care of herself and the house, too. Some days, if her parents did not reach home on time, she would even cook supper.

One day, Jenny went to the park to play. A girl came up to Jenny and asked, "Are you new here?" Jenny shook her head and told her about the housework she had to do. The girl said, "You should not feel bad. Your parents work hard all day, you should help them. We can play together in your free time." This made Jenny very happy.

17. The Two Sisters

Lucy and Meg were sisters. One day when they returned from the park, their mother said, "Girls, please wash your hands and come to the table." Meg, the younger of the two girls said, "I don't want to wash up, Mother!" Their mother said, "It is best for you to clean your hands after playing outside. Look at those hands. They are so dirty. You cannot have your pancakes with dirty hands." "I don't think I need to wash my hands. will be eating with fork and knife!" said Meg.

Lucy was watching this quietly. She told her sister, "Meg, your hands have brought dirt from outside. Just look at them. Do you know, how many germs live in dirt? They are on your hands now."

Meg was scared. She looked at her hands and said, "Oh, no! I didn't know that!" "Come with me. I shall help you wash your hands," said Lucy. The girls washed their hands and Meg felt better and cleaner. Their mother was very proud of her wise little daughters.

18. New Friends

Dora loved her elder sister, Bess. She followed Bess wherever she went. Dora liked to be with Bess even when she played with her friends. Soon, Bess was bored of having Dora around all the time. She wanted to play alone with her friends sometimes.

So, Bess said, "Dora, it is time that you make your own friends. You'll have fun with little girls of your age." But Dora did not know how to make friends. She was scared to go out and talk to other children.

Bess then took Dora to the park one evening. There, she saw her dear friend, Laura and her little sister, Kelly. She introduced Dora and Kelly. The four girls played together for a while Dora and Kelly became best friends and they also made other friends at the park. Bess was very happy for her sister.

19. True Friends

Jane and Georgia were very good friends. They spent the entire day at school together. One day, a new student, Elmer joined their school. He and Jane soon became friends. Elmer was very rich. He told her about the games and toys he had. Jane was fascinated by his stories.

One day, Jane asked, "Elmer, can I come home to see your toys?" Elmer agreed but Georgia did not want Jane to go. Jane did not listen and went with Elmer. Elmer took Jane to his room and showed her the toys. Jane really liked the toys but broke one of them by mistake. Immediately, Elmer shouted, "You silly girl! You have ruined my toy. Get out of my house."

Jane was hurt and ran home. Georgia wiped her tears and comforted her. Then, she said, "It takes time to get to know people and to make friends."

Jane was thankful that she had Georgia as a friend.

20. Catherine and the Door

Catherine was a careless and silly young rabbit. Whenever she went out, she often forgot to close the door behind her. One day, she had to go out of the house to buy lunch for her husband, Joseph.

As Catherine was leaving for the market, Joseph said, "Don't forget the door, my dear."

Catherine thought about her husband's words and an idea came to her. *The best way not to forget the door is to take it with me!*

Thus, Catherine took off the door from its hinges and heaved it on her back. She went to the market carrying the door. Everybody started laughing at her.

Catherine realised that Joseph had wanted her to close the door and not take it with her. *I will be more careful now and pay attention to what others tell me,* she decided.

21. Patience

One Sunday, Miss Evans told the children, "Patience is a very important virtue that all human beings should have. Never lose your patience children, and you will never quarrel or be sad."

While walking home, Carrie overheard Belle and Jenny arguing. Carrie reminded them of the lesson they had learnt that day.

That evening, her brother Charlie, took her book to read, as he found his own book rather boring. This made Carrie very angry and she snatched it out of his hand.

As soon as she opened the book, she saw the sentence, "You need to have patience." Carrie immediately realised that she should practise what she preached.

22. Ice cream Trouble

Meg was a very helpful, sweet girl. She loved to play with her friends. One day, she went over to her friend Jane's house to play. Soon, the ice cream man came to their street.

Jane asked her mother to buy her ice cream. But her mother did not have money. So she said, "When your father is back, we shall go to the store and buy ice cream." Jane was very upset at this and started crying. She would not listen to her mother. Her mother did not know what to do. Meg felt very sorry for Jane and her mother. She said, "Come Jane, we will go to my house. I think my father is at home."

The girls went to Meg's house and asked her father for ice cream. He bought them ice cream and made Jane promise that she would never trouble her mother again. Now the girls were happy.

23. Mia and Josie

Josie was playing in the park when she found a red ball. *A little red ball! I will keep it for myself,* thought Josie. She kicked the ball all over the park and had fun. As she was playing, she heard someone crying bitterly. She turned around and saw a small girl crying. She said, "Hello, I am Josie. Why are you crying?" The small girl said through big, weepy eyes, "I am Mia. I have lost my favourite red ball." Josie was confused.

Should I return the ball or keep it for myself? she thought. *It belongs to her and she is so sad!*

So, Josie showed the ball to Mia and asked, "Is this your ball?" "Oh! Yes! Thank you!" said Mia and took the ball. Her face was shining happily now.

Mia and Josie became friends. Every day, they played with the little red ball together.

24. Sara and the Angel

Once, a little girl, Sara lived with her parents in a little cottage. Her father was a thief and her mother worked all day.

Sara prayed to God every day to help her. One day, she woke up in the night. She saw a beautiful angel.

The angel said, "Dear Sara, you prayed to God with a pure heart every day. So, He has sent me to help you." Sara said, "I want my father to stop stealing, work responsibly and love me." The angel granted her wish. The next day, Sara found her father near her bed. He apologised and went to look for work. Soon, he started working on a farm. Also, he started loving Sara and always kept her happy.

25. The Jealous Friend

Two girls, Jane and Maria grew up together and went to the same school. Jane was very nice but Maria was mean. She envied Jane. She never thought well for Jane. On the other hand, Jane loved Maria as a true friend.

One day, Maria forced Jane to steal apples from her neighbour's orchard. Suddenly, Maria heard the guard coming and jumped the boundary wall to get out of the orchard. But, Jane got locked inside. After a while, the guard saw Maria outside and asked, "Did you see anybody enter inside?" Mean Maria told the guard about Jane. The guard searched, but could not find Jane. When Maria left for home, she found Jane standing outside her house.

Jane said, "I heard you and sneaked out before the guard could find me. You are a dishonest friend. I never want to see you again!" Maria had lost a good friend because of her dishonesty and jealousy.

26. The Man on the Hill

Once, a naughty girl lived in a village. She broke pots, made cattle run away and added lots of salt in food to trouble others. She caused trouble in the entire village. People were fed up and decided to teach her a lesson. One day, the girl was playing. A few men went to her and said, "A man with an abnormally large body lives on the hill top. He sleeps all day. If you wake him, we will give you gold." The girl was very happy. She agreed and went to the hill top.

There, she saw the man sleeping. She tickled him by putting pieces of grass in his ear and nose. The man got up. He caught hold of the girl and shouted, "How dare you wake me up?"

The girl was terrified and wanted to run. But the man kept her imprisoned for a day to teach her a lesson. Once the girl returned home, she became very well behaved and was pleasant and helpful to others.

27. You Get What You Give

Once, a little girl went out to play in the evening. On the way, she saw an ice cream seller. He had a lovely red cart with pictures of mouth-watering desserts. He called out loudly to attract children, "Strawberry, vanilla, chocolate and butterscotch... Come and take any of them!"

The girl went near the cart. She searched her pockets for money, but only found a few nuts. The sly seller gave her the oldest orange bar and took the nuts.

After the girl walked away with the ice cream, the seller started eating the nuts. When he ate them, he realised that all of them were stale. He was disappointed but understood that you get what you give.

28. It's a Round World

One day, Mary was crossing a river. The shoe from her left foot fell into the water. Mary was very sad, her mother would now be angry and even punish her. She went home, unhappy. A man who was fishing caught Mary's shoe instead of a fish. He left it on the bank of the river.

A pigeon scooped the shoe from the bank and flew away with it. On the way, the shoe slipped from the pigeon's beak. It landed in a garden where some people were having a picnic. A little boy picked up the shoe and threw it over the fence into a cowshed.

The shoe's lace was caught on a cow's horn. The shoe was now hanging from the cow's horn. The milkman saw this and threw it into a farmhouse. This was Mary's farmhouse. Mary saw it a little while later. She happily thought that the world was indeed round!

29. The Boy and the Sparrows

Once, there was a beautiful
Rosebush that covered the wall
of a farmhouse. Close to it lived a
family of Sparrows in their nest.

One day, the Mother-Sparrow
was caught by some boys, who put
her and her children in a cage. The
Mother Sparrow was very sad
to see her little, playful children
sitting sad and alone in the cage.
She began to sing a sad lullaby to
put them to sleep.

The neighbour's son, Sammy was a kind-hearted and gentle
boy who loved birds. He quietly crept in through the open window
and set all the birds free. The birds thanked Sammy and happily
flew away to their nest.

30. The Orphan Girls

Linda and Tracy lived in an orphanage. The manager made the girls work all day and
gave them very little to eat. Linda and Tracy were very unhappy and ran away from the
orphanage. The next day, they reached a new town. There, Linda and
Tracy heard two women saying that the queen was hiring maids for
the palace. They went to the palace and were immediately hired. They
were very happy and worked hard. They always took care of the
queen. She started depending on them greatly.

After sometime, the queen's evil aunt invited her for
dinner. Linda and Tracy advised, "Do not trust her.
You could send one of us and see how your aunt treats
us." The queen did as advised and sent Linda. To the
queen's dismay, they found that the aunt imprisoned
Linda. The queen sent her guards immediately to get
Linda released. She then thanked Linda and Tracy and
kept them as her chief advisors!

31. Redelfa Learns a Lesson

Redelfa was a German princess, the elder child of her parents, and was extremely spoilt. She liked to waste her time carelessly. Redelfa's mother, the queen, was old and worried about her daughter's careless behaviour. She called Redelfa to her chamber and said, "Dear daughter! Since we do not have a son, you will be the next queen. It is time you learn to perform your duties sincerely." Redelfa listened to her mother absent-mindedly, and continued to waste time and money.

Soon, the time came to declare the next queen. The old queen surprised everyone by declaring Mitchell, her stepdaughter, as the next queen. Mitchell was a responsible and humble girl. Everyone was overjoyed at the news. Redelfa was ashamed when the news of the new queen spread across the land. She had learnt her lesson!

32. Good Deeds

Sarah was a very rich woman. Yet, she was never content. She always wanted more things. She thought, *I can buy anything!*

One day, Sarah decided to buy a house of gold. She went to many people and asked, "Please tell me the way to a shop that sells gold houses." But, no one could help her.

After some time, Sarah saw an old man and asked the same question. He asked, "Do you help the needy? Do you teach poor children? Do you read to the old?" Confused, Sarah replied, "No, I don't do any of those things."

The old man said, "You will have a house of gold, if you do them." Thus, Sarah started helping the poor and the old. These good deeds made her very happy. She knew what the old man meant. By doing the good deeds, her heart had become a house of gold!

33. The Magical Skipping Rope

Once, there was a very lazy princess. She never exercised. She ate and slept all day long. Soon, she fell sick. The queen called the royal doctor to examine her. The doctor knew that the princess's problem was her laziness. But it would be very rude to tell her that. So, the doctor made a plan. He gave the princess a skipping rope and said, "This is magical. Skip with it for half an hour in the morning and half an hour in the evening. You will feel better soon."

The princess did not know that it was an exercise. Thinking that it was a treatment prescribed to her, she followed it regularly. Within a few days, the princess became very healthy and fit. She asked the royal doctor, "How did the magic work?" The doctor said, "It is not magic. You need to exercise your body regularly so that you never fall ill again."

34. Meg

Molly was a sheepdog and helped the Farmer keep a track of his sheep. The Farmer always praised Molly for her work.

Molly's daughter, Meg watched her work and wanted to help. But, Molly felt that she was too young to work.

One day, Molly was helping the Farmer to put all the sheep into a big pen. "Good girl, Molly!" said the Farmer, closing the gate and patting her on the head.

Suddenly, Meg saw a lamb slip through a crack in the gate and run away. Meg barked to inform but Molly and the Farmer did not notice.

So, Meg ran behind the lamb and saw it stuck in a hedge. Then, she went back and led the Farmer forcefully to the hedge. The Farmer took the lamb home. Then, he said, "Good girl, Meg!"

Meg was very happy that she had helped the Farmer, too! And Molly did not feel that Meg was young any more!

35. The Golden Goose

Once, an inn keeper lived with his two daughters. One day, a traveller came to stay in his inn. He carried a beautiful goose with golden feathers. The girls wanted to touch the golden goose.

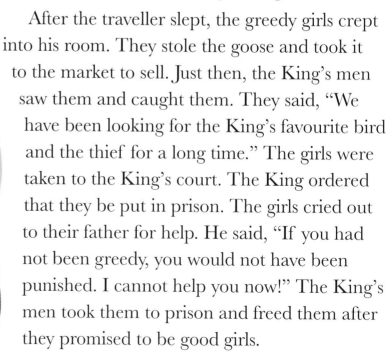

After the traveller slept, the greedy girls crept into his room. They stole the goose and took it to the market to sell. Just then, the King's men saw them and caught them. They said, "We have been looking for the King's favourite bird and the thief for a long time." The girls were taken to the King's court. The King ordered that they be put in prison. The girls cried out to their father for help. He said, "If you had not been greedy, you would not have been punished. I cannot help you now!" The King's men took them to prison and freed them after they promised to be good girls.

36. The Elf's Gift

Maria's Father worked in the King's army. He had gone to fight the battle to defeat the enemies.

One day, Maria found a bottle on the beach. She opened the cork and lo, a tiny Elf jumped out! He said, "You saved my life! Ask me for one wish!"

Maria wanted a pretty doll but she said, "Can I think and tell you tomorrow?"

The Elf agreed and Maria went home. Her Mother was waiting for her at home. Teary-eyed, she told her that her Father had been wounded at the battlefield. Maria started crying and prayed to God.

The next day, she ran to the beach and said to the Elf, "Please save my Father's life! Please bring him back home!"

The Elf quietly vanished. Maria sadly returned home. When she reached home, her Father was actually lying on the bed. Maria jumped with joy and hugged him, tight.

37. The Miser and His Gold

Once, there was a rich farmer, who had a large farm. However, he was a miser. One day, the miser bought a brick of gold from the goldsmith. He was worried that someone might steal his treasure. Thus, he buried his gold underneath a tree. He then visited the tree every day to check on his gold. Once, a clever servant followed the miser. Then one night, the servant went to the tree. He dug around it and found the gold. He quickly ran away with it.

The next day, the miser went to the tree and saw that his gold had been stolen. He started crying loudly. His wife came out running and he told her about the missing gold. She said, "Do not cry! Now bury a stone near the tree. Think it is your gold, and be happy. You were never going to use the gold anyway!"

38. The Happy Family

Once there was an old estate where no one lived. Burdocks covered the estate garden. Burdock leaves were used in ancient times to breed Great White Snails, which were made into delicious stews and eaten by the royal family.

Now, the last two surviving White Snails lived in the garden. They were left, because nobody lived in the estate any more. The White Snail couple did not have any children of their own, so they adopted a little Common Snail and brought it up. The couple loved their adopted son. They got him married to another Common Snail and left the whole garden to the young couple.

The young couple had numerous children. They all lived in the garden as a happy family.

39. The Generous Woman

Many years ago, a queen and her army fought a long battle. After the victory, they decided to return to the palace. On the way, their food got finished. Everybody was very hungry. So, the queen ordered, "Minister, go to the largest farm and get all the fruits." The minister stopped a woman and said, "Take me to the largest farm to pick fruits."

The woman led him to a farm. The minister and other soldiers picked all the fruits that they could find. Then the minister asked the woman, "Is this the largest farm?"

The woman replied, "No, this is my farm. I could not take you to somebody else's property knowing that you will pick everything that grows there."

The minister was touched and praised the woman's generosity in front of the queen. The queen rewarded her with two big farms to spend the rest of her life happily.

40. The Poor Shoemaker

Once, a poor shoemaker and his wife lived in a small cottage. One day, he could not complete an order, due to fever. His wife got really worried, as the customer was going to come the next day to take his shoes. Next morning, the shoemaker and his wife were surprised to see the shoes made. The client came and paid a good price for them.

The shoemaker and his wife wondered, *Who made the shoes at night?* They decided to keep a watch. At midnight, they saw, two elves enter from the window and complete the shoemaker's orders. The next day, the shoemaker and his wife made two pairs of clothes and little shoes for the elves and kept them on the table. The elves came and saw their gifts. They were extremely happy. After that, they made sure that the shoemaker and his wife never faced any trouble.

41. Naughty Lizzie

Lizzie lived with her parents and little brother. She was very naughty and was scolded all day by her mother. One day, she pinched her brother while he was asleep. He got up and cried. Lizzie's mother locked her in the room. After some time, Lizzie's grandmother came home. Lizzie heard her mother complain about her to the grandmother. She was very ashamed.

Then, grandmother came to her room. She said, "You should not do all these naughty things, my child. Everybody will love you if you learn to behave." Now, Lizzie decided to be a good girl. She went to school on time and studied hard. Also, Lizzie did all her homework and helped her mother with the household tasks. Her parents were pleasantly surprised with her behaviour.

They bought her many new toys. Lizzie was very happy and thought, *Being good really pays off.*

42 . The Useful Cat

Once, a wise old man lived with his son. Before dying, he said, "Son, I don't have anything to give you except my cat. But, I assure you that you can make money if you use it wisely." The son did not know what to do with the cat and decided to sell it.

He travelled from one village to another, but could not find a buyer. Finally, he reached the king's palace. The king was sitting unhappily in the garden. The son asked him, "Why are you upset?" He replied, "A naughty rat entered my room and is creating havoc. All the servants have failed to catch him." The son left his cat in the king's room. The cat caught the rat and killed it.

The king was very pleased and kept the son and his cat in the palace. The son spent the rest of his life in great comfort.

43. The Ugly Duckling

In the countryside, a Mother Duck sat on her nest containing five eggs. Finally, there was a Crack! Little ducklings came out of the eggs, except for one. A little gray creature came out of that egg. It was ugly and large.

The Mother Duck took her children to meet the other ducks. When they saw the Ugly Duckling, everyone made fun of him. Tired of being teased and made fun of, he went to a moor where they treated him worse. Everywhere he went, he was treated badly because he was ugly. Autumn and winter passed away like this.

Finally, in spring, he was swimming in the water. Miserably, he saw his reflection. He was not ugly any more! He was a graceful, beautiful swan now! He swam around with the other swans while children threw cake and bread to him.

He never called anyone ugly, because he knew that all creatures were beautiful.

44. The Poor Girl

Maria studied in the local school. Every day, she noticed a poor beggar girl looking sad and standing outside her school. She would go to talk to the girl, but the girl would run away, as if scared. Then, for a few days, Maria did not see the girl at all. One evening, Maria was going to the circus with her parents. On the main road, she saw the girl again. Maria ran to her and asked her what she was doing there. The girl said that she lived with her ailing mother and was begging for money to buy her mother's medicine.

Maria's parents were very kind. They at once took the girl's mother to a hospital. Then, they took the girl home with them. When the girl's mother was well, she started working in Maria's house. And so, the girl and her mother started living in Maria's house. The poor girl now went to school with her every day and there was finally a smile on her face.

45. Joan's Delay

One day, a group of little girls was playing at the park. They were having so much fun that they did not realise how much time went by. The sun was setting already. Suddenly, one of the girls, Elizabeth, noticed that it was getting dark. She told her friends that it was probably time to go home.

All of them, except Joan, agreed and they went home. Joan enjoyed playing on the swing so much that she did not want to leave. Soon, it was night and almost supper-time. Joan's mother called at their friends' and neighbours' houses and asked them if Joan was there. She was very worried and went to the park. She found Joan playing on the swing and told her, "Joan, you are still here. I have been worried sick. I called your friends to find out what happened. You should always return home before dark."

Joan saw how worried her Mother was. She felt guilty and promised to be home on time.

46. Cousin Janet's Problem

There was once a naughty girl called Pommy. The children in her class were afraid of her. Her teachers had given up hope of making her a well-mannered girl. People tried to teach her good manners, but she would not change. Pommy's cousin, Janet was very troubled by her behaviour and prayed for her.

One day, Janet's mother asked her to carry some buttermilk for her Aunt Nancy. On her way, Janet saw a cow blocking the path. She was very afraid of cows and began to shout for help. Suddenly, Pommy came and chased away the cow with a stick. Pommy then went with Janet to Aunt Nancy's house, in case there were more cows on the way. She also walked back home with her.

Janet's mother thanked and praised her a lot. Even her friends and neighbours praised her for helping her cousin. Pommy felt very good at all the attention and love she got. From that day on, Pommy changed and became a nice girl.

47. Bertha's Grandmother

Bertha Gilbert lived with her family in a little village called Hillside. One day, her wealthy friend Holly visited Bertha's house with her mother. While having tea, Bertha was embarrassed at the old, worn-out furniture they had. She glanced at her grandmother. She wore simple clothes and was knitting quietly. Holly and her mother, on the other hand, wore bright dresses of silk and precious jewels. Bertha also noticed Holly look at the house and make faces. She was not pleased.

After the guests had left Bertha went to her mother and said, "Grandma should wear fancy clothes. Holly was making faces at her." Mother was very upset with Bertha. She said, "Bertha, you should respect people the way they are and not for what they wear."

Bertha felt ashamed of herself, for her grandmother was wise, caring and loving. She also decided not to have ill-mannered friends like Holly, any more.

48. The Paper Kite

A beautiful paper kite was flying high in the sky. It was brightly coloured, with curly tassels and a long string. The kite was so high up that it was giddy with excitement.

The kite thought, *O look at me flying so gracefully! If I were free, I could go far away.*

The kite tugged at its string, as it wanted to fly right through the clouds and above the eagles. However, the string was strong and held it tight.

The kite impatiently tugged at its string again and again and the string broke.

The kite was full of joy. It tried to fly higher, but suddenly it started falling. Free of its string, it had become heavy and lost control. It drifted towards the sea and was washed away in the tide.

The paper kite cried, "I wanted to fly higher and higher. Look, what I got for being so proud!"

49. Jealous Mrs. Plum

Mrs. Plum was jealous of beautiful Mrs. Peach. One day, she invited Mrs. Peach over for dinner. She made soup for dinner but put a lot of chillies in it.

When Mrs. Peach arrived, Mrs. Plum greeted her politely and was very nice to her. However, she really wanted Mrs. Peach to eat the soup full of chillies and burn her throat. Soon, she served the soup. Like a true lady, Mrs. Peach did not complain.

Later, Mrs. Peach invited Mrs. Plum to have dessert at her place. Mrs. Peach baked a pie, but put a lot of salt in it. Thus, when she served it to Mrs. Plum, she found it very salty and could not eat any of it.

Now, Mrs. Plum began to cry. To this, Mrs. Peach said, "If you play dirty tricks on people, then you must expect them to do the same to you."

50. The Proud Lady and the Caterpillar

One day, a young lady was walking in her beautiful garden and admiring the colourful flowers. Suddenly, she saw a caterpillar on her dress. She was horrified.

The lady shook him off her dress, saying angrily, "Go away, you ugly caterpillar! You eat all the leaves, flowers and fruits and ruin my lovely garden. I work so hard to keep my garden beautiful. You spoil it by being here."

The caterpillar looked at her and said calmly, "Proud lady, the lovely silk of your dress has come from insects like me, so do not insult me. I am ugly to look at now. Soon, I shall turn into a beautiful butterfly. Your beauty is temporary and depends only on the clothes you wear. I am beautiful from inside, and when I become a butterfly I will be more beautiful than you!"

51. The Grateful Eagle

Once, there lived a kind girl named Beth. One day, she went to the forest to collect firewood. On the way, she saw an eagle caught in a trap. She at once set it free and walked on. Beth became tired and sat down on a rock on top of a hill. The eagle was flying close by and she saw that the rock was loose and would roll down the hill, taking Beth with it. Thus, while Beth was having her lunch, the eagle swooped down and snatched her hat. It then flew away with it. Beth stood up and ran down the hill after the bird.

Just as Beth reached a safe distance away from the rock on which she had been sitting, it rolled down the hill with a loud crash. She realised then that the grateful eagle had paid back for her kindness. Then on, Beth and the eagle became good friends.

52. Patty's Secret

Patty had been very sick and had to go to the doctor many times in the past. She would be scared earlier. However, now she was very brave and always smiled in the hospital. One day, Patty overheard her Aunt tell her parents about a sick girl who was afraid of visiting the doctor.

Patty went to visit this little girl with her parents. Patty said to the girl, "I have to go to the doctor many times and I used to be very scared. But one night I had a dream where I saw God. He told me not to worry. Then when I visited the doctor the next time, I felt God put his hand on my head and say, 'Patty, I am taking away your fear and pain.'

The girl was no longer scared, for she knew God was taking away her fear and pain, too, just like he did Patty's.

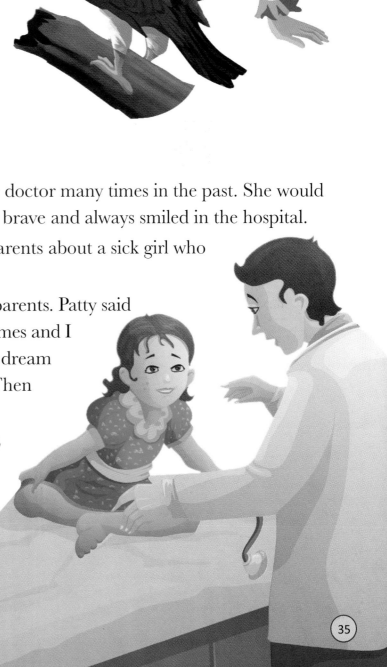

53. The Lonely Man and the Fairy

Once, there lived a man who had no family and so he was very sad. The man had a beautiful garden with a lovely pond, which was now becoming dirty. One night, he hid in the bushes and at midnight, he saw some fairies descending from the sky. They took off their wings and put them aside. Then they splashed each other with mud and water. The man quietly stole a pair of wings. When the sun was about to rise, the fairies returned to their homes in the clouds. However, the fairy whose wings the man had stolen, was left behind.

The man said to her, "I want to marry you. But if you want to go home I won't stop you." The fairy saw that the man was kind. She had been lonely too, so she agreed to marry him. The two were happily married. The man wasn't lonely any more.

54. Secret

Once, a girl lived with her mother. The mother gave her good values and advised her to be honest, always. One day, the daughter came back from school with tears in her eyes. The mother got worried and asked her the reason. The daughter did not tell anything and went to her room.

A little later, she came out and hugged her mother. The mother asked, "What happened, my darling?" She replied, "I failed in my exams. The result came last week but I did not tell you. Now the Principal does not want me to attend the school."

The mother said, "A daughter should never keep a secret from her mother. If she does, then she definitely gets into trouble."

The daughter apologised and promised to be honest in future. The next day, her mother went and convinced the Principal to let her daughter attend school.

55. The Three Witches

Once, there were three witches. They troubled people and stole from them. One day, the three witches robbed a sack of gold from a wealthy merchant's house. Then they all went deep into a forest outside the town to divide the gold amongst themselves. When they reached the forest, they felt hungry.

So, a witch went back to the town to steal food. There she stole from the bakery and had a tasty meal. Then she mixed poison in two cakes for the other two witches, because she wanted to keep all the gold.

Meanwhile, in the forest, the other two witches were hiding behind a tree. When the first witch arrived there they killed her. Then, they happily sat down to eat the cakes she had brought. But, as soon as they ate them, they fell dead because of the poison.

Thus, all the witches became victims of their evil ways.

56. Dora's Lesson

Once, there lived a young girl named Dora, who was never content with what she had.

One day, Dora found a nut. She tried to bite it but it was very hard. Her tiny teeth could not cut into it. She said, "Oh Lord! Why did you give me such tiny teeth?" God heard Dora and said, "Dear Dora, look at other creatures. I will give you the teeth of any creature you like."

So, Dora went in search of different creatures. Finally, she saw the teeth of an elephant. She loved the ivory white teeth of the elephant. She said, "Wow! What beautiful teeth you have!"

At this, the elephant said, "My teeth are just for show. I cannot use them for chewing. I simply have to bear the heavy weight of my teeth." Dora, at once, realised her mistake and thanked God for her natural teeth.

57. Beautiful Earth

The kindergarten class of Pinkville visited the forest to enjoy a day picnic. There, one of the little girls asked their teacher, Mrs. Goodwill, "How come some places have many trees and some none, Mrs. Goodwill?"

Mrs. Goodwill replied, "When our beautiful Earth was created, there were many green fields, full of grass and trees. God also created birds and animals to live in the meadows and the fields. Finally, He created man to take care of all the beautiful creations."

"God warned the human race to be good beings; otherwise the Earth would lose all its beauty. However, when Man came to Earth, he forgot God's warning. He started stealing, lying and killing others. That is why the Earth is not as beautiful everywhere, anymore."

The kindergarten class felt very ashamed. They decided to be nice and honest people, to make the Earth a beautiful place again.

58. Night-time Adventure

Once, a girl named Elizabeth studied at a boarding school. She was very naughty and did not like to go to bed early. Thus, every night, she would jump over the boarding school's boundary wall and wander about in the night.

Elizabeth thought that no one knew of her secret. However, wise Mrs. Smith, the history teacher, knew it. She wanted to catch Elizabeth red-handed.

One night, Elizabeth sneaked out as usual. She climbed up a ladder and jumped over the wall. When she had gone, Mrs. Smith removed the ladder.

A few hours later, Elizabeth returned. She panicked when she saw that the ladder was missing. Suddenly, Mrs. Smith emerged from behind the bushes. She said, "Elizabeth, you should take a warm shawl when you wander out in the night, or you will catch a cold." This made Elizabeth ashamed of herself. She became a sincere student after this.

59. Mary and the Man

Once, a beautiful girl called Mary was unkind to people. Her parents were very angry at her behaviour. Thus, her father married her to the ugliest man in the kingdom.

Mary was very angry but she had to go and live with him in his hut. The man was kind to Mary, but Mary was rude to him. Time passed, and Mary realised that the man cared a lot for her.

One day, the man was chopping wood and hurt his hand. When Mary saw him in pain, she started crying, for she loved the man. Lo! He suddenly changed to a handsome Prince.

Just then, a Queen appeared before them and said, "Mary, this ugly man is my son, the Prince. He was cursed by an evil witch and became ugly. Only true love could have rescued him. You saved my son!" Mary and the Prince lived happily ever after.

60. The Most Wonderful Doll

A poor girl, Maria, lived with her mother and father. One day, she saw a rich girl, Jenny, standing in a toyshop.

Jenny's father bought her a big doll. Maria felt very sad because she did not have a single toy. Maria's mother said, "Don't be sad. Your father will make you a beautiful doll, soon." Maria's father was a carpenter. When Maria reached home, her mother asked her father to make a wooden doll for her. The next day, Maria's father gave Maria a present. It was a beautiful wooden doll.

Maria was very unhappy, for she wanted a fancy doll like Jenny's!

Just then, she saw that her father's hand was hurt. Maria understood that her father had hurt his hand while making a doll for her. She at once went to him and said lovingly, "Father, this is the most wonderful doll ever. I love it!"

61. Love for a Daughter

Once, a man lived with his wife and daughter. Unfortunately, their village got flooded and the wife died in the flood.

The man decided to leave the village and go to a town in search of work. He took his money and left with his daughter. On the way, robbers attacked him. They took all his money. Suddenly, they saw the man's little daughter tied to his back. She looked like an angel. They said, "If you want to save your life, give us your daughter."

The man fell on his knees and cried, "I don't want to live without my daughter. So, kill me before you snatch her away."

The robbers were deeply touched to see that the man was ready to die for his daughter. Then they thought of their own daughters and how they would suffer if they died. So they gave up stealing and went back home.

62. The Sun and the Moon

A long time ago, the Sun and the Moon were a married couple and lived happily on the Earth. They were best friends with the Sea and visited him every day.

One day, they decided to call the Sea for dinner. The Sea hesitated and said, "There will not be enough room for me in your house."

The Sun and Moon assured him, "We have a big house. You will not have any problem there."

So, the Sea went for dinner with all the members of his family. As they entered the house, the water began to rise.

The Sun and the Moon got scared. The Sun held his lovely Moon and climbed on the roof of their house. But, the water kept rising and they finally climbed up to the sky. Since that day, this lovely couple left the Earth. Now, they like living in the sky!

63. The Wise Old Lady

Once, an old lady lived in a village. One day a hermit visited her. The old lady served him very well. So, the hermit gave her a magic lamp. After the hermit left, the old lady rubbed the lamp. A Genie appeared and said, "I am your slave. Give me work or I'll eat everything around me."

The old lady asked the Genie to grow crops in her field. The Genie completed the task quickly and came back to the old lady for more work.

Now the old lady was worried since she did not have more work. She said, "Straighten my dog's tail. You cannot rest till you have finished this task."

The Genie tried for many days, but could not straighten the tail of the dog. He grew tired and apologised to the old lady. She forgave him and they lived as friends thereafter.

64. Silly Fights

Once, many girls played in a park. One day, two girls had a fierce fight. These two girls started gathering supporters from among the other girls in the park. Soon, two groups were formed. Slowly, the two groups started disliking and fighting with each other every other day.

One day, one group of girls went to the big, mean girl and said, "Some girls of the park have become our enemies. Please come to our park and trouble them." She happily agreed to do so.

Thus, the big, mean girl troubled the girls of the enemy group. She even took their sweets and toys. The girls asked her to leave the park. But she refused for she liked to snatch the goodies from little girls! So, she stayed in the park and troubled all the girls. Then both the fighting groups realised their mistake and chased the mean girl away. All of them then became friends and played happily together as before.

65. Useless Pride

Jean and Kitty were two friends. Kitty made iron statues and Jean made jewellery.
One day, Jean and Kitty were going to the town with their ponies. Jean's pony had silk cloth on its back. It was carrying gold coins and precious gems in two large sacks.

Kitty's pony was simple. It was carrying some iron tools in its sacks. Jean's pony was full of pride because it was carrying precious goods. Kitty's pony was calm.

As they were passing through a forest, some bandits stopped them. Jean and Kitty ran away, leaving their ponies behind. The bandits searched the ponies. As they found nothing valuable on Kitty's pony, they let it go.

Then, they saw Jean's pony standing stiff with pride. They understood that it had valuable goods. And so, they carried it away with all the jewels!

66. Proud Linda

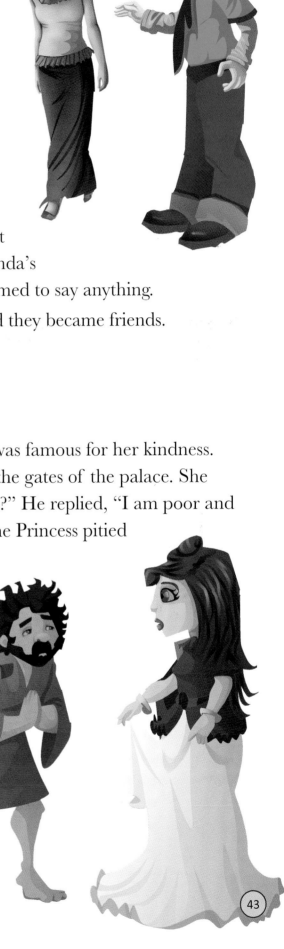

Once, a beautiful but proud girl, Linda studied in a school. She made sure that she made only pretty and rich friends. One day, her school planned a picnic. Linda and her friends were very excited. They went for the picnic and had a lot of fun. One of her classmates, Ben, came to her and asked, "Will you play with me?" Linda looked at him and said scornfully, "I don't like to talk to ugly people like you."

Ben felt very bad, but did not say a word. After some time, he heard a loud shriek. He ran and saw that Linda had fallen into the lake and was drowning. Without wasting any time, Ben jumped into the lake and saved Linda's life. All the students praised Ben, but Linda was too ashamed to say anything.

The next day, she apologised to Ben in the school and they became friends.

67. Intelligent Princess

Long ago, a Princess lived in a magnificent palace. She was famous for her kindness. One day, she noticed a beggar rubbing his back against the gates of the palace. She asked, "Why are you rubbing your back against our gate?" He replied, "I am poor and have not had a bath for days. So, my back is itching." The Princess pitied him and gave him twenty gold coins. This news spread through the kingdom.

A few days later, the Princess saw two beggars rubbing their backs against the gates. She ordered, "Give these beggars twenty whiplashes to cure the itch." They cried, "You gave the other beggar twenty gold coins. Why are you punishing us?"

The Princess replied, "He was alone, so he could not scratch his own back. But you both can scratch each other's backs and are here because of greed."

The two beggars felt really ashamed.

68. The Mirror

Belle was a pretty girl who lived in the village. She would help the poor, teach the children and read to the old.

Once, a White Fairy visited the village. She saw Belle and observed how helpful she was. The White Fairy decided to test her and bewitched Belle's mirror.

When Belle saw her reflection in the mirror, she screamed in terror. She looked very frightening now! Her pretty face was large and swollen, her blue eyes were now red and her nose was a pig-like snout.

The Mirror said, "I shall turn your face pretty, again, only if you promise to be rude and cruel to everyone."

But, Belle said, "No! I shall live with this ugly face, but will not stop helping my people." Suddenly, the mirror shattered and the White Fairy appeared, smiling. She said, "Dear Belle, you have passed my test." and gave Belle magical healing powers.

69. The Cruel Lady's Fate

Once, there lived an old woman. She would beg alms from the villagers, every day. Even though she was poor, she was very generous and would share with the needy.

One day, the old woman reached a rich, but cruel lady's house. The cruel lady rudely said, "I don't have anything for you!" The old woman said, "Please help me, for I am poor." So, the cruel lady angrily went inside. She mixed poison in some leftover food and gave it to her. The old woman took the food to the riverside. As she was about to eat, a little boy came and said, "I am hungry."

The old woman gave all the food to the boy. But, she was shocked when he ate the food and became very sick.

Later, she found out that the little boy was the cruel lady's son. The cruel lady's evil deeds had resulted in the poisoning of her own son!

70. Careless Jenna

Jenna was a rich, but foolish girl. She would trust strangers and was careless with her money.

One day, Jenna visited the town. There, she saw a café. It was warm and beautiful. It smelled of delicious coffee. Jenna decided to buy the café. She asked a man, nearby, "Excuse me, sir. I want to buy this café in a hundred gold coins. Where can I find the owner?" The man said, "I am the owner. Give me the gold and the café is yours." Thus, he took the money and went away.

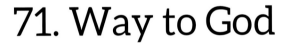

Jenna happily walked inside the café and said to the waiters, "Kind fellows, I am the new owner of this café." A lady said, "Says who? This café is mine!"

Jenna was taken aback. Now she realised that the man was a liar and had duped her. She decided to be careful with strangers from that day on.

71. Way to God

Once, there was a church in a village. People came and prayed there on Sundays. The Father was a noble man and showed the people "the way to God".

A young woman, Lily, came to church every Sunday. After the prayers, she talked to the Father for long hours and discussed various religious issues. Lily told Father, "I pray regularly to God. I do a lot of charity and show people the right path." One day, the Father decided to test her. He asked a beggar to beg Lily for alms.

The beggar asked Lily for some food. She did not bother and entered the church. The beggar followed her and begged again. Lily got irritated and asked the beggar to leave her alone, and get out of the church.

Now, the Father came out and said, "Lily, you can never reach God if you are cruel to others." Lily was ashamed.

72. The Impatient Girls

Once, a woman lived with her three daughters. The girls were very impatient and never listened to their mother.

One day, it was the birthday of the youngest girl. The mother prepared her favourite strawberry cake. When the cake was baked, the mother took it out of the oven. She topped it with chocolate icing. Then, she decorated the cake with little red roses.

The girls' mouths watered when they saw it. "Dear mother, kind mother, hurry up and give us a slice!" the impatient girls begged her.

"Wait until it cools down and you can eat it all, otherwise, your tongue will burn," said the mother.

However, the impatient girls could not wait and tried to eat it hot. The moment they put the pieces of the cake in their mouths, their tongues were burnt! They went to their mother and cried in pain, "Oh! We will always obey you!"

73. Elizabeth's Wish

Elizabeth was unhappy. She lived in a small house in the city of Oaktown. Elizabeth wished her father had more money to get her everything she wished for. Every day, Elizabeth's parents sat on their porch at sunset. She would play in the garden. One evening, the sunset was just gorgeous. Mother said, "Elizabeth, see how beautiful the sunset is!" But Elizabeth was lost in her thoughts. She said, "Father, I see the beautiful house with the golden windows over there. Why can't we have a house like that?" "Come, I'll take you up the hill to see the house," said Dad. As they climbed up the hill, the golden windows disappeared.

Elizabeth realised that the sun's rays had made the windows look golden. Now she understood that money and riches are only good from a distance. Close up, they are ordinary things and one should not be unhappy for money.

74. The Magic Pot

Once, a girl lived with her mother. They were very poor and had nothing to eat. One evening, the girl met an old lady who gave her a little pot and said, "Take this pot and say, 'Cook, little pot', it will cook good sweet porridge. To stop it, say, 'Stop, little pot'."

The girl went home and tried the pot. The pot was soon full of sweet porridge. The girl and her mother ate happily. Then, one day the girl had gone out, when her mother said to the pot, "Cook, little pot." The pot cooked sweet porridge, and she ate it.

She forgot what to say to the pot to stop cooking. So the pot continued cooking till it spilt over and reached the street. Everyone in the village was shocked and ran to the house. When they came to know about the reason the porridge was spilling on to the streets, a search party was sent out to find the girl as the mother would not have been able to find her alone.

Finally, the girl was found and brought home where she stopped the giant spill by saying, "Stop, little pot." The pot stopped cooking at once and the villagers jumped with joy! From that day, every Sunday the entire village got together for a bowl of porridge and the joy of togetherness at the request of the girl.

75. The Girl and the Evil Wizard

Once, a wizard kidnapped the eldest sister from a house where three pretty girls lived. However, one day, she disobeyed him and entered a small room he had not wanted anyone to see. The angry wizard fed her a poisonous potion and locked her in the room.

The second sister was also imprisoned by the wizard in the same way. The third sister was very clever. She obeyed the wizard and he asked her to marry him. However, the girl secretly went to the room, used the remaining potion the wizard had, and brought her sisters back to life.

Then, the girl packed a huge basket with gold and hid her sisters in it. She asked the wizard to take the gift to her house. When he went, she covered herself with honey and feathers and disguised as a 'Fitcher's Bird' she escaped to her house.

When the wizard returned, the girls' brothers followed him. They locked the house from outside and left the evil wizard to his fate.

76. The Clever Reply

Once, there lived a clever poetess named Misha. She told the Queen, "I dreamt that you are the Queen of Queens. My dream will come true." The Queen was very happy and gave Misha a hundred gold coins. On her way home, one coin slipped and fell in a hole. Misha started looking for it.

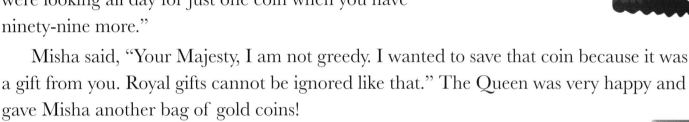

In the evening, the Queen saw Misha on the road and asked her what she was doing. Misha replied, "I lost one of the coins and am not able to find it."

The Queen said, "You are very greedy. You were looking all day for just one coin when you have ninety-nine more."

Misha said, "Your Majesty, I am not greedy. I wanted to save that coin because it was a gift from you. Royal gifts cannot be ignored like that." The Queen was very happy and gave Misha another bag of gold coins!

77. Brave May

Once, a girl named May lived with her parents and her little sister, Susan. One day, May decided to go for a walk over the bridge. Susan also wanted to go but her mother refused, as she was very naughty. Susan started crying. So, May requested her mother, "Do not worry! I'll take care of her."

The mother was hesitant, but agreed. Happily, the two sisters started walking to the park through the bridge. But, naughty Susan left her sister's hand as soon as she reached over the bridge. May ran behind her.

Suddenly Susan's foot slipped and she was about to fall into the river. But, May ran just in time and grabbed her hand. Susan was saved but May was badly hurt. She had bruises all over. Some people, who were passing by, carried both the sisters home and told the parents about May's bravery.

The parents kissed and thanked May for saving Susan's life.

78. The Smart Donkey

A washerman went to the river every day to wash clothes. He sat on his donkey and rode on it.

The people of the village made fun of him. They said, "Look at that. A fool is riding another fool."

The washerman said, "My donkey is not a fool. He is smarter than the king's ministers."

The news of the washerman's comment reached the king very soon. The king called for him and asked, "Why do you think your donkey is smarter than my ministers?"

The washerman said, "Your Majesty, one day, while crossing the bridge, my donkey's feet got caught between the wooden boards. From that day, whenever he reaches that spot, he is very careful. Your ministers spend a lot of your money, but they have still not repaired the bridge. So, my donkey is smarter." The king realised that his ministers were not doing their jobs.

79. The Greedy Woman

Cindy lived with her old aunt. The aunt made the poor girl work all day and never gave her enough to eat.

One night, Cindy could not sleep due to hunger. She left the house and went to the forest to pick some fruits. Suddenly, she saw some robbers hiding some gold and money behind a rock.

She waited quietly till the robbers left. Then, she took away some coins. She went home and gave them to her aunt.

The aunt asked her about the place. She was a greedy woman and wanted to take all the coins. So, at night she went to the forest to steal more. By then, the robbers knew that somebody had stolen their gold.

They were waiting and caught the aunt. Cindy pleaded before them to set her aunt free since she had no other relative in the world. The robbers' heart filled with pity at Cindy's plight and they set her aunt free. The aunt was very ashamed. She took good care of Cindy from then on.

80. The Sparrow and Her Children

Once, a sparrow went off to find food for her four children. When she came back, she found them missing. She was worried, as the children were very young.

A few days later, the children came back. The sparrow asked them how they had managed to live on their own. The eldest son told her that he stayed in a garden and ate caterpillars and other small worms. The second son had lived among the stable boys and fed on grains or corns. The third son had spent the summers on roads and ate the grains of barley. The sparrow advised them to be careful with all these places, as these places were dangerous.

Then, the youngest son told her that he lived in a church and fed on the spiders and flies. The sparrow happily said, "He who lives in God's shelter is always safe."

81. A Cottage in the Mountains

Bella lived in a cottage in the mountains. The mountains were covered with grass and trees and looked very green.

In the spring, flowers would bloom all over. Then, the green mountains would be speckled with pink, blue, purple, orange, yellow and red. Bella looked at the mountains and enjoyed their beauty.

Bella would sit under the shady trees and read her books. When she felt hungry, she picked juicy berries from the trees and ate them.

Sometimes, it rained in the mountains. The mountains looked lush and green. Bella would put her arm out of her cottage window and enjoy the raindrops on her palm. When the sun shone after the rains, a large and beautiful rainbow would appear in the sky. It had seven colours that glowed in the sun. Bella loved her home and was very happy that she did not live in the city.

Her cousin had insisted she come to the city and live there. Bella had gone there for a month but did not like the hustle and bustle of city life. So, she came back. She was grateful for her home in the mountains.

82. Janine's Magic

Once, there was a woman called Janine. She had no job, so she went to the nearby town and told everyone that she could do magic.

One day, some thieves struck in the town and robbed many houses in one night. The people went to Janine for help.

Though she could not perform any magic, Janine could not admit the truth. She had to agree to help them. She asked every town member to come to her one by one, so that she could identify the thief. When the first man came, Janine said, "Oh, you are the first man," meaning that he was the first person who had come to see her. But, the villager was actually the first thief! He was shocked and terrified. He fell at Janine's feet and revealed the names of the other thieves.

The happy people rewarded Janine with gold coins.

83. Katie and Beauty

Once, a girl named Katie lived with her parents on a big farm. Her father gave Katie a beautiful pony, Beauty, on her birthday. She was extremely happy and wanted to ride immediately. Her father warned her, "Beauty is a naughty pony. Also, you are not a good rider yet. So, you should not go alone to ride him."

Then, he promised to take her for a ride the next day. Katie was disheartened. But, she did not say anything. When everybody slept at night, she quietly went to the stable. Then, she took Beauty out and tried to ride him.

Beauty was not friendly with her and kicked her hard as she went to sit on it. Katie fell on the ground and cried loudly.

She had broken her leg and could not ride Beauty for the next three months. Katie was ashamed that she had not listened to her father.

84. The Hen and the Cock

Once, a hen and a cock were friends. They both went to a hill to collect nuts. They decided to share the nuts they found. Soon, the hen found a large nut. However, the selfish hen ate it all. The nut was so big that she choked on it. She shouted to the cock to get her some water.

The cock ran to the stream, but the stream demanded some silk from a bride. The cock went to a bride, but she demanded a wreath from a tree. After giving the bride and the stream what they wanted, he went back to the hen with water. As soon as the hen drank the water, the nut that was stuck in her throat went down to her stomach. The hen felt guilty at not having shared the nut with the cock.

The next day, the hen found another big nut. She gave the whole nut to the cock who ate it happily. The hen felt very pleased and always shared her food with the cock.

85. The Magical Dove

Once, there was a young girl who got lost in a forest, while picking flowers. Unknowingly, she went deep into the forest and could not find her way out. Tired, she sat under a tree and wept.

Suddenly, a white dove flew down and dropped a key on her lap. To her astonishment, the key spoke! It guided her to a tiny lock on the tree. She opened it and found a room where she could eat and rest. Then, the dove flew away.

The next day, the white dove returned and asked the girl for help. The girl readily agreed. The white dove led her to a witch's cottage and told her to fetch a ring from there, without the witch's knowledge. The fearless girl got the ring and suddenly the cottage turned into a palace and the dove into a prince! She had broken the witch's spell. The prince and the girl married, and lived happily ever after.

86. Stupid Janet

Once, a girl named Ann lived in a beautiful mansion. She was very rich and proud.

One day, her best friend, Janet came to visit her. She said, "I am getting married to Mr. Philips soon." Ann was disappointed and said, "Dear Janet, you are my best friend. You should not get married to an ordinary man like Mr. Philips. I will find you a better match."

Janet broke her engagement and Ann advised her to pursue Mr. Rogers who was a wealthy man. Janet did as told but Mr. Rogers found Janet too ordinary. Thus, he rejected her proposal.

Janet was heart-broken. She went to Ann for sympathy. But now, Ann had no time for her. Poor Janet was completely alone. She did not use her own mind and acted on her proud friend's will. Therefore, she suffered and could not get married for a long time.

87. Alice

Once, a poor girl, Alice lived with her mother. Her mother worked extremely hard to send her to a good school. However, Alice always felt ashamed of being poor. She always demanded money for new things. One day, Alice's mother fell ill and wanted to visit the doctor, but Alice insisted that she wanted money for the school picnic. Mother explained, "If I give you this money, I will not have anything left to buy the medicines." Alice did not bother about her mother's health and forced her to give the money.

When Alice came back from the picnic, she found her mother lying unconscious on the floor. She rushed her to the doctor's house. Her mother stayed in bed for several days before she was well again.

Alice hated herself for being selfish. She promised her mother that she would study well and also help in her work during her free time.

88. Boastful Dina

Dina was a very brash and dishonest girl. She would tell tall tales to her friends about false adventures and trips. Soon, Dina's friends became tired of her lies and started ignoring her whenever she spoke. Thus, Dina decided to go and stay with her aunt in Bournville during her summer holidays. A few months later, Dina returned from Bournville.

One day, she invited all her friends to tea. Just as they all sat down to tea, Dina said, "In Bournville, I jumped so high, I was out of sight! If you don't believe me, go and ask anyone who was there."

"There is no need," said a girl. "Why don't you pretend you are in Bournville and jump out of sight right now?"

Everybody started laughing. Dina realised that people hated her lies. She felt ashamed of herself and decided to remain honest from that day on.

89. Lynda and the Songbird

Once a kind-hearted girl called Lynda was walking through a forest path. Suddenly, she saw a beautiful golden songbird caught in a net that had been spread by the bird catcher.

The songbird was crying for help. Lynda ran and freed the bird. The songbird chirped joyfully and flew away.

One day, Lynda was sitting on a wall and eating her lunch. Suddenly, the same songbird swooped at her food and took it away. Lynda jumped to snatch her food back, but lost her balance. She fell down the wall.

She felt very angry at the ungrateful songbird. Then, she saw a poisonous snake slithering down the wall. The songbird had saved her from being bitten!

90. Ashley and Max

Ashley had a very naughty brother, Max. He troubled Ashley all the time and played many pranks on her.

One day, Max and his friends hung a bucket full of ice-cold water on the door. They tied it with a string and decided to pull the string as soon as Ashley entered the room, so that the water would fall on her.

When Max heard Ashley come near the room, he climbed on the chair to pull the string. But, he could not maintain his balance and fell down from the chair. All the water fell on him and he caught a cold and fever.

Now, he had to stay in bed for a few days. Ashley felt very bad for her brother and did as much as she could to look after him. Max was very touched and apologised to his sister. He never played any pranks on her again.

91. Twelve Birds

Once, a king and a queen had twelve sons. The king was cursed that when his thirteenth child was born, he would kill all his sons. Thus, when the queen gave birth to a girl, she sent her sons to hide in the forest. However, the princess grew up and went to live in the forest with her brothers.

One day, the princess mistakenly plucked twelve magical flowers. Her brothers at once turned into birds. Just then, she heard a voice, "If you want your brothers back, remain silent for seven years."

One day, a king saw the princess and married her. Just then the seven years of her vow to remain silent also ended and the new queen's brothers were free from the spell. They came and blessed their sister. The siblings were united and they all lived happily together.

92. The Stolen Orange

There was once a girl called Flora. One day, some guests were coming to Flora's house. Flora was busy cleaning her room. Just then, she passed the kitchen and saw oranges piled up in a dish. Flora was not allowed to eat those oranges, as her mother had bought them for the guests. But, she took one and hid it in her pocket.

However, she knew she had done the wrong thing by stealing. Flora wanted to return the orange but the guests arrived and she became busy. She had to play with their children.

Flora could not enjoy any of the games. She kept thinking of how shameful it would be, if the orange fell out of her pocket while they were playing! Or if she sat on it by mistake! After dinner, Flora went to her mother. She told her what she had done and asked for her forgiveness. Her mother was very happy at her honesty. She hugged Flora and forgave her.

93. Christmas Presents

It was Christmas Eve. The Smith family had put up their glorious six-feet Christmas tree in the living room. It was decorated with fir and pine cones, coloured eggshells, and different shapes cut out of craft paper. The shapes looked like snowflakes. There was a beautiful star on top.

In the evening, the Smith family enjoyed a delicious six-course dinner. Grace and Bella helped their mother clean up after dinner. Then, they hung up their stockings and left cookies and milk by the fireplace for Santa Claus. They went to bed, hoping Santa would leave presents for them.

Grace and Bella's parents knew that they had been good children all year. After the girls were asleep, they put big presents under the Christmas tree for them. In the morning, Grace and Bella were very happy. They decided to be good children next year, too.

94. Manor Farm

Manor Farm was a huge, secret forest. All the creatures in that forest respected Europa, the unicorn. One day, Europa called for a meeting. She said, "I want a life in which all the creatures live together with no Dragon to control us."

The creatures were thrilled and welcomed Europa's idea. However, three nights later, Europa died. All creatures were very sad and depressed now. But, three young Centaurs decided to work on Europa's dream and make it come true.

The other creatures hesitated, as they did not trust the youngsters as much as the old wise Europa. But, the Centaurs convinced them. They made a plan and explained it to all the creatures.

So, one night, the creatures attacked the Dragon and chased him away from the secret forest. All agreed that if it were not for the young Centaurs, they would never have been free.

95. Serena and Leona

Once, Serena took her sister, Leona's chocolate from her bag and ate it. Leona was very angry and decided to take revenge.

The next day, when Serena came home from school, her mother shouted, "How many times have I told you not to leave your room in a mess?"

Serena ran upstairs and was horrified to see the condition of the room. She tidied the mess and knew that Leona had done it. Once, after school, Serena and her friends fought with Leona. Leona cried all the way home and told her mother what had happened.

When Serena came home, mother said, "Girls, you are blessed to have each other to depend on. Love and forgive each other for you will be with each other all your life. If you won't take care of each other, you will both suffer."

The girls promised their mother that they would never fight.

96. Friends at School

Belle was a rich, spoilt girl. She went to a boarding school in London. Her friends were also spoilt and would do anything for her.

One day, a girl named Fannie joined their school. She wore dirty clothes, was shabbily dressed and wore an old hat on. Everyone could see that Fannie was poor. Belle and her friends made fun of poor Fannie whenever they got a chance. Fannie was very upset and hurt by their bullying. She was scared to talk to them.

One day, there was a poetry recitation competition and everyone participated. Fannie recited a beautiful poem about friends and friendship. The students were amazed because her poem was the best in the class.

Belle realised her mistake. Fannie was poor but very nice and talented. Belle apologised to her for her mean behaviour. Fannie forgave her and they became good friends.

97. Generous Anna

Anna felt like having an ice cream. She went and looked for her moneybox. But it had no money. "Oh! No! It's empty," she said. So, she went to her mother and asked, "Mother, can I have some money to buy an ice cream? The ice cream man is in our street." "What happened to the money in your moneybox?" asked her mother. "I bought some flowers for little Lizzy who is sick and in bed, with that money. Look, it is empty," and she showed mother her empty box. "I will give you some money. Come with me," said mother. Anna's mother gave her the money. When Anna went to buy the ice cream, her friend was crying, "My mother has gone to Grandma's and will return next week. I miss her!"

So Anna bought the ice cream and gave it to her friend. She stopped crying and enjoyed the ice cream. Anna was glad that her friend was happy again.

98. Fair Josie

Josie was a pretty, fair little girl, but was also vain. *I am the most beautiful. So, I deserve the prettiest things!* she would think. She would not let her friends touch her toys. Soon, Josie's friends became fed up of her. They stopped visiting her. Now, Josie was very sad. She did not understand why her friends would not talk to her any more.

Weeping, Josie ran to the backyard and sat among the grape vines. Suddenly, one of the grapes started glowing purple. The light became brighter and turned into a beautiful woman dressed in purple clothes.

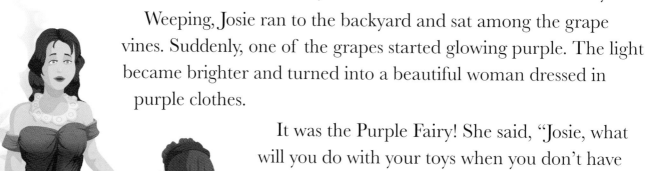

It was the Purple Fairy! She said, "Josie, what will you do with your toys when you don't have friends to share them with? Do not be vain, and share your things. You will be happier!" and she turned back into a grape.

Josie learnt her lesson and apologised to her friends.

99. Emma and Sophie

Emma and Sophie were sisters. Emma was a quiet girl and loved to read. She never went out to play. Sophie was just the opposite. She was always outside, playing with her friends. She never spent any time at home.

Their mother said, "Emma, you should go outside and play with Sophie for some time. And Sophie, you should learn to sit down and read for at least an hour every day."

So, Emma decided to go out to play with Sophie. Sophie showed her a lot of fun games that Emma never knew about. Emma enjoyed playing outdoors.

Then, when they came home, Sophie said, "Emma can you help me pick a book to read?" Emma said, "Let's read together, Sophie. This is a very funny book." The sisters enjoyed reading the book. They understood how much fun it was to be with each other. Their mother was very happy.

100. Grumpy Nancy

Nancy, the grumpy fairy lived in the fairyland. She found faults with everyone.

One day, she went to buy some bread. The Baker Fairy gave her the best bread, but Nancy told her, "The bread does not look good! It seems you don't know how to bake bread." The Baker Fairy said, "You are very rude. I don't want to talk to you." Similarly, Nancy spoke rudely to all the other fairies and upset them. They stopped talking and doing any work for her.

Now Nancy had to do all the work on her own. Also, she felt sad and lonely. After a few days, she went to the Queen Fairy and complained. The Queen Fairy said, "Nobody wants to be friends with a grumpy person. If you show love and respect to others, they will also show love to you."

Nancy realised her mistake and improved her behaviour. Soon, everybody forgave her and started talking to her again.

101. Careless Janine

Lisa and Joan were best friends. They went for a picnic near a river and took a basket of food and some toys. Joan's little sister, Janine, also wanted to go with them.

The girls said, "You can come but promise to stay near us." Janine readily promised.

When Janine saw that the other two were busy, she quietly went into the nearby forest and soon lost her way. She started crying and shouting for help. Soon, Joan and Lisa found her sitting under a tree repenting her actions. When Janine saw the two friends she shouted with joy! Janine decided to always listen to them and never break a promise again.